The Adventures of Jake Hawks

THE BIGFOOT SAGA

JAKE HAWKS

ISBN: 979-8-89031-526-7 (sc)
ISBN: 979-8-89031-527-4 (hc)
ISBN: 979-8-89031-528-1 (e)

Because of the dynamic nature of the Internet, any web addresses or links contained in this book may have changed since publication and may no longer be valid. The views expressed in this work are solely those of the author and do not necessarily reflect the views of the publisher, and the publisher hereby disclaims any responsibility for them.

THE EWINGS
PUBLISHING

One Galleria Blvd., Suite 1900, Metairie, LA 70001
(504) 702-6708
1-888-421-2397

Chapter 1

L et me introduce myself. My name is Jake Hawks. Allow me to tell you a story about an adventure that my friends and I experienced.

The story begins at my friend's house; his name is Gary, and we call him Duke because he looks like John Wayne and he carries himself like him. My other friend is Duke's son. His name is Trampas and we call him Two Slim, because he is tall and slim. While I was visiting them, they asked me if I would like to go on a camping and fishing trip deep in the Arizona mountains, because they know I like to fish. I've been fishing most of my life, and so I accepted the invitation and we started to make plans to go on this trip. We decided to take my Jeep Rubicon because it can go deep into the mountains off road. We set the date up for the second week in September and so we were set. I knew that I would try to make contact with a Bigfoot. I always believed in them, that they really existed. I felt this way since the 1970s. As I packed my Jeep, I put in a baseball bat to bang on trees, hoping to get a response from Bigfoot or the big guy. I went to pick up Duke and Trampas at their house. We loaded the Jeep and left. The trip was about five hours or more. We traveled from southern New Mexico from the high desert barren terrain north to Santa Fe and west to Arizona. The terrain went from barren to some grass to some big trees to beautiful pine trees. As we went and crossed over from New Mexico to Arizona, the landscape was awe-inspiring. As we traveled deeper and deeper into the mountains of Arizona, the trees got thicker bigger and denser. Up until then we were on the paved roads until we found the correct turn to go on an old logging road that hasn't been used in years.

Before I continue on, let me digress a little. Allow me to tell you how I met Duke and his son Trampas.

One day my wife, Toni, and I were driving on a desolate road, just driving around to see what's around, and we passed what looked like a town of some sort. We pulled off the road and decided to check out this old western town. As we were walking around, a man who was about six foot, three inches tall started to walk towards us. He had on a six-shooter and was carrying a Winchester Repeater rifle. As we were talking he gave us his name, which was Gary, but he wanted to be called Duke. The name of his town is Boot Heel. He told us that he built this town and it took him thirty years to complete. For some reason, he and I took to liking each other right away, being so close in age. We spent the next four hours with him as he told us his life story. I won't bore you with all of the details, just some. Duke was in Vietnam and he was in the Army as a Green Beret. So that alone tells you a lot about the person that is called Duke. Now, let me talk about Trampas. He is about thirty years old and he knows his way around a campsite—not a bad guy to bring on a camping and fishing trip. Now let's get back to the trip.

As we went off the paved road onto the old logging road, the road itself was getting hard to maneuver around all of the downed trees and damage from the flooding that happened over the years. At one point I had a heck of a time moving even in my Jeep. We knew that there was a secluded lake a few more miles in where the fishing would be excellent, so we kept on going until we arrived. It took more time than we expected it would take. We barely had enough sunlight to set up camp. As I stated before, the lake is very secluded and there was absolutely no one around. We had the lake and surrounding area to ourselves, or so we thought. When we settled in, started a camp fire, and ate and started to talk, we noticed a smell of what we thought was a skunk but different—more musty. I couldn't compare it to anything but rotting garbage, but not quite like that either. The smell was moving around. We thought the wind had changed direction. At the time, we didn't think anything of it; we just continued to have some laughs. We all were tired from the trip so we turned in for the night. At about one in the morning, we heard footsteps walking around in the camp, which woke us up. In the morning we were talking about what had happened the night before. No damage was done to the campsite or anything else. I thought it was Duke walking around and he thought it was me. The feeling was that we should be more on guard the next night. We then started our day of fishing. During the day, I couldn't shake the feeling that we were being watched. I couldn't see anything around the camp, but we all felt that eerie feeling that we were being watched. We spoke about it during lunch and no one had seen anything. We had a great lunch of fresh trout. We had caught too many fish, so we put our poles away for the day and just sat around the campsite catching sunrays. Just an hour before dusk, we started to fish again as is that is a good time to fish. We only caught a few trout, enough for supper. There is nothing like eating fresh fish. We had started the campfire again and were just sitting around when we heard something moving around in the bushes behind the campsite. We shone the light from the flashlight to see if we could see anything, but we didn't. We decide to get our handguns on just in case whatever was out there came into camp. Nothing happened for hours so we went to sleep. Again in the middle of the night we heard footsteps moving around in our camp; nothing else happened that night but in the morning all of the fish that we left were gone. We presumed that whatever came into our camp just wanted the fish to eat.

As we began our day we started to fish and at the lake's edge I noticed some tracks in the soft ground. It looked like human footprints, but the size was enormous. I asked Duke if he had a tape measure so we could see how big the prints were. He said he didn't have one but Trampas had one. We measured the prints; they were eighteen inches long and eight inches wide and sunk into the soft ground almost two inches. The interesting thing about the print that I noticed was the animal had a mid-tarsal break in the foot. We were all amazed at the size and asked each other what animal could have left prints so big. The only thing that I could think of was Bigfoot. I couldn't believe how lucky we were to be having some kind of contact with that Bigfoot person. Nothing else happened for the rest of that day and our last night, as we were leaving the next morning. At the campfire that night we were deciding what time we were going to pack out and leave. It was decided that we would get some last hours of fishing in before we left. As we sat around the campfire it was all so quiet—too quiet. There was no forest noise, no wind, and no insects making their noise, nor elk making their sounds. It was so quiet that you could hear a pin drop. I must confess that it spooked all of us and put us all on edge. We didn't know what to make of what was going on or what was going to happen while we were sleeping. As it turned out, we had a quiet night and had a great night's sleep.

Just before dawn on our last time to fish, I was out on the lake's edge fishing for trout. Duke and Trampas were standing in front of the tents when it happened. We heard a blood-curdling scream from what I guess was a Bigfoot, which was followed by coyotes answering that scream with howl of their own. I knew the scream was from a Bigfoot, first because I've heard that kind of scream on television and because the coyotes answered that scream. I yelled back to my two camping companions "that was a Bigfoot that just screamed." The scream was very close to our camp, so we decided to pack out right then and not wait any more. We didn't know what was going to happen next so we packed up as fast as we could. We packed the Jeep and flew out of the area. What this means is that Bigfoot was close enough to hear our conversation around the campfire on the last night. So Bigfoot knew we were leaving that next morning.

The ride home was very interesting because Duke and Trampas never believed in Bigfoot and kept asking me if I was sure it was Bigfoot. I assured them that it was and re-stated the two reasons why. Also on the way home I remembered that I read that most times, Bigfoot would do something on your last day to put a scare into you so you don't ever come back. It worked: Duke and Trampas said that they would never go back to that spot. Me that's another story. All I wanted to do was to go back and try to see one close up and take a few pictures.

Chapter 2

Since I had the close encounter with Bigfoot, I decided to research the Bigfoot phenomenon more fully than I had before. I went to the library and took out all of the Bigfoot books I could get my hands on. I went online and was able to find many websites that had to do with this phenomenon. I was able to subscribe to a newsletter called Bigfoot Times by Daniel Perez, which was very informative. Here is his e-mail address: perez952@ sbcglobal.net.

I looked at all of the photos that I was able to get, to download, read all that I could find from many authors. During my reading I came to a hypothesis and here it is:

I feel that Bigfoot can read people like kids or dogs can. They can tell if a person is good or not. Call it a sense, but they can and are drawn to them. Right or wrong this is how I feel and there is more.

I have seen many picture of tree structures and to me it looks like the Bigfoot are trying to make an Indian dream catcher. So what am I going to do with these feelings? I'm going to find one to show the scientific community that the Bigfoot's are real. I don't want to harm any one of them in any way. I feel that Bigfoot are individuals like you and I and they have different personalities. They can communicate through the mind as the Holy Spirit does. So how can I prove that my theories are correct?

I need to go on an expedition. I need to find someone who is capable to go on one. I need to find someone who can finance this expedition. It must be done in the right time of year. There are so many questions that have to be answered.

The first thing I need to do is find a backer to finance this expedition. I do have someone in mind, but I haven't spoken to him in a very long time. His name is Jimmy P and he owns a semi-conductor company in California. How do I ask him for money to back this project? I called him and it was like old times. We spoke about what we used to do, like playing Pac-Man together and stopping to have bagels. During our chatting it came out that he took up golf and I told him that I play, too. He asked me if I wanted to play a round when I arrive and of course I said yes. He wanted to know where I would like to play. I said Pebble Beach so he made the arrangements. I also mentioned that I need to talk to him about a project. I let him know that I would be flying in. I checked on a flight and would be flying into San Diego international on SSBI Airlines flight 554, at nine on Monday morning. When I arrived, I went to get a taxi and to my surprise Jimmy sent a car to pick me up, and not your ordinary car, but a big stretch limousine. The driver put my luggage and clubs into the car and we were off to

Pebble Beach to play. Pebble Beach has been a dream of mine, but I couldn't afford $500 a round. I would never have that kind of money. Pebble Beach was on my bucket list and now I could scratch it off. As the limousine arrived at Pebble, it was an awesome, beautiful sight. Someone comes and takes your clubs out of the car, puts them on the golf cart, then cleans the clubs before you even play. I was surprised at that but for $500 a round, that's what is done.

As we were playing I started to talk about the project and Jimmy said, "wait until we have dinner and we will discuss it then." We finished the round and I must say that the views there are amazing. It was hard to concentrate on playing. Every hole was a picture. Jimmy said that he would send the car to pick me up at seven for dinner.

Seven came and sure enough the limousine was in front of my hotel. The limousine took me to a fancy place and Jimmy was already there. We ordered dinner and as we were waiting for dinner to arrive, I started to tell Jimmy about the project. He wanted to know all about Bigfoot—how big they were, where they live, how many of them are in the USA. I told him that the full grown adults are between ten and twelve feet tall and weigh about 800 pounds or more. The older ones don't interact with humans. The ones that are five feet to eight feet tall do interact with humans mostly to have fun but sometimes humans get too close to their homes so they try to protect the homes just like we would do. Scare them off, so to say. I said that there are about 2,000 to 6,000 in North America. He was quite intrigued. So here is my plan.

The Crew is going to be five or six men who know how to handle themselves in tough situations, to camp and rough it for a minimum of three weeks. They must have survival skills with no modern conveniences, be able to make knots with rope. They have to be physically fit and be able to hike for miles. Once we find the camp, we must look for signs that Bigfoot is around in the area. We will look at whether there is enough food in the area to sustain a large predator. We will look for bear, deer, elk, and other animals that can be eaten. We'll search for berries, nuts, or farms in the area and fruit tree orchards, too.

Then we will look for any tree structures, snap offs, footprints, and places that a Bigfoot lair could be in, such as caves.

We will have food for the Bigfoot to eat and we will set a trap, by hanging a bag of food such as fruit about twelve feet high so only a Bigfoot will be able to reach it. On the ground there will be a net made of two-inch thick, high strength cobalt polypropylene rope with the break strength of 78,000 pounds. The Bigfoot will trip this net and the net will spring upwards, catching the Bigfoot. We will have a helicopter at our disposal to airlift the Bigfoot to a secure location. There he will be tranquillized so we can control him. Scientists will be called in, some tests will be made (nothing to harm him), and he will be released back where he was removed from.

Jimmy asked how much this will cost, and I said about five million dollars for two weeks. The helicopter is where the big cost comes from. Jimmy said that he doesn't know if spending that kind of money is worth the cost. I told him that to find out that there is a higher primate on the Earth beside ourselves is a scientific breakthrough of our lifetimes. That it could be a relative of Gigantopithecus, a giant ape from China that is ten feet tall. That Bigfoot is a live fossil from prehistoric times. I did the best I could to convince him. He said that he would let me know very soon. With that I left and took a plane back to New Mexico, waiting for his decision.

While I was waiting I had to find five or six men that could do the job that is required of them for this task. I had a few in mind. Should I wait to hear from Jimmy or just go ahead? I decided to go ahead and find these men.

The first one I asked to join this crew is Texas Jack Henry, who likes to be called Texas Jack. He's six feet, three inches tall and weighs about 265 pounds. He has been a camper, Eagle Scout and is one mean SOB, but a good friend of mine.

Next is Arkansas Tom Willis. Tom is about six feet, two inches tall and weighs about the same Texas Jack. Arkansas is a hunter of bear, elk, and mule deer and is built like a brick shit house. But he is as nice as he is big.

Third is Rattlesnake Bill Thompson. Bill is about six feet, one inch tall and weighs 245 pounds. Rattlesnake is a trapper and fisherman. He likes to spend time in the backcountry being alone. I met Bill, I mean Rattlesnake, when I was on a fishing trip. Rattlesnake is his alter ego. He is a nice man who would give you the shirt off his back.

Fourth is Cory 'Torch' Arp. Don't let the name fool you. Cory likes to be called Torch. He is a hunter, fisherman. He welds steel for a living and loves riding his motorcycles all over the country. This is someone who is a nice guy but you don't want to get on his bad side. He will eat you up and spit you out. My old friend Duke introduced me to him. He is about six feet tall and weighs about 195 pounds. He's good to have if you're in a jam. You can always depend on him.

It'd been almost been a week since I met with Jimmy P. I had to give him a call to find out what he wants to do. I still had to find two more men to make this team complete. I couldn't move forward until I got an answer from Jimmy. I was hoping that he was going to come on board with this expedition. I did have two guys in mind but I was not going to ask them until I found out either way.

I finally heard from Jimmy P. He said he would finance the expedition under one condition, that the Bigfoot or Sasquatch would be put on the endangered species list. I agreed to that. I was sure that we can get Dr. Luis Rivas to help us with that and to be one of the scientists to identify the Sasquatch into the unknown species list. Dr. Rivas is the foremost scientist in the field of Cryptozoology and his charge is to gather other scientists that can assist him in his endeavor to identify this new species.

Well were all set except for the last two men for the team. When that was accomplished then we could go head and make plans to get started with the expedition. All the other men were getting very excited about what was going to happen on this trip deep into the wilderness. I knew what could happen, but I wouldn't let anyone know that it could mean a life or death situation at times.

Chapter 3

Someone had told me about these two men who were outdoorsmen and able to take care of themselves in any situation. I arranged a meeting with them both to discuss the expedition to see if they had any experience with Bigfoot or even if they heard of Bigfoot. To them, it didn't matter. They just wanted a chance to look into the unknown and be explorers of a kind. Their names are Darren Albrecht and Matt Smith. Darren likes to be called Daz and Matt, just Matt. Both of these men fit what was needed for this expedition. The team was complete and ready to go.

All of the team must meet before we start this expedition, to get to know each other and to make sure that we all get along, which is very important. We had to learn to work as a team. Considering the situations that we were all going to be in, we had to depend on one another to get the job done, to make sure no one gets hurt or killed.

The team asked me what they should expect when confronting a Bigfoot. An adult Bigfoot is between ten feet and twelve feet tall, weighing 800 to 1000 pounds, and can snap you in half like a twig. The Bigfoot do not have the same personality; they are different just like us. They migrate from place to place following the food source. They stay in family groups, from adults to juveniles to the very young. The young ones climb trees, too.

We all met and disgussed what supplies were needed. Everyone had different ideas as to what to buy to keep us healthy and safe. No one was supposed to get hurt on this trip. We all agreed on the supplies such as water, food, flashlights, rope, tents, sleeping bags, knives, pistols, rifles for protection against other wild animals, and tranquilizer guns. Once the supplies were procured we decided the best time and place for our expedition. I told them of the incident that happened to Duke and myself and we as a group decided to go deeper in the mountains near a water supply, such as a lake or river. The Pacific Northwest was the place that we picked. In Northern California there is a lake called Lake McClure. Lakes McClure and McSwain are nestled in the scenic Sierra Nevada foothills of Central California where pine and oak trees flourish—located just below the magnificent Yosemite National Park in Merced and Mariposa Counties, California.

That's the place where the expedition would take place. We decided to go during the second week of September, since most of the tourists should be gone, and kids have to go back to school. We only had to wait a few weeks and we would be off. We still had to get some more equipment so the extra time helped us prepare.

Chapter 4

We were going to take three vehicles, all four wheel drive. The trip to Northern California would take twelve hours or more. Then, we'd drive to Lake McClure. We figured that it's going to take a day just to drive and find a suitable campsite and then find a spot to set the trap to catch the Bigfoot. Just to set the trap would take hours and lots of manpower. That's why I need big men.

As we got to the lake we started to unpack the pickups and we were looking around with binoculars to see if we could find a spot to camp at. Nothing was close so we started to go deeper into the woods, away from the lake. The more we got away from the lake the more we would have to trek back for water. Remember that we would be out there for about three weeks or less, depending on how fast we trap a Sasquatch. We were one mile away from the lake and still had not found a suitable place, when we came over this rise and the land became flat. We were three miles from the pickups, and we all decided that this was the place to set up camp. I placed a large dream catcher high on one of the trees to see if it would draw in a Bigfoot. I did this to see if my theory was correct. The night passed without incident.

In the morning I was looking through the binoculars and I thought I saw a small river about half a mile away from where we set up camp. I checked the maps but there was no river on the map that feed into the lake. So I decided to go and see what was out there.

I took one of the guys with me. Cory (Torch) came to keep me company. As we were walking and looking around for any signs of Bigfoot we didn't see anything until we got about a mile from camp and there was a small river about 200 yards away. We started towards the river. I noticed some snap offs on the way and some tree structures so I knew that the Bigfoot were here. We kept going toward the river and when we got to the river, I noticed that smell of rotting garbage or a skunk smell. I told Cory there was a Bigfoot close by. He asked me how I knew that and my reply was, "notice the smell and the signs that we came upon." The signs such as the snap offs and the tree structures told me that we were on the right track. Add in this bad smell, and I knew we were close. I told Cory to go back and get some of the guys and bring them back here. Also, make it as fast as you can; double time it NOW.

As I was waiting for Cory and some of the guys, I walked down to the river area just to take a look and low and behold, there were Bigfoot tracks that went on for twenty-five feet. Usually Bigfoot like to cover their tracks as they don't like to leave any signs that they were around. They are that smart. I think because no one was around the Bigfoot didn't think about that. I knelt down and I noticed that there was a large print and a smaller one, too. That smell got stronger, so I had the feeling that I was being watched. I stood up and looked around and saw nothing. I couldn't shake the feeling that I was being watched. It had been fifteen minutes and Torch brought back with him Texas Jack and Rattlesnake Bill. Torch had let Jack and Bill know what was going on with the Bigfoot. Torch showed them the Bigfoot signs on the way to meet me. When they got to me I showed them the tracks and they were amazed at the size of the tracks and then I showed them the smaller ones. They asked "is there a family of them here?" I said it looked like there was a family group.

This time I came prepared. I said to Texas Jack, "get the plaster so we can make casts of the prints." He asked where the plaster is, and I said it's in my truck and told him to bring some water to mix the plaster. The rest of us prepared the prints and took pictures of the track way while Texas Jack went for the plaster. The prints were the best I've seen. It's too bad I didn't have the plaster to cast the tracks from the lake. When Jack got back with the plaster I asked him to mix the plaster with water and to pour the plaster into the footprints. The plaster sets up in twenty minutes, so we all scouted the area looking for a spot to set the trap. We did leave one guard to make sure that nothing happened to the plaster. Rattlesnake Bill was left as the guard hoping that nothing came around to disturb the plaster casts.

When we came back to collect the plaster casts, Rattlesnake Bill was not around. We all took a quick look to find Bill, but he was gone. We thought maybe he went back to the camp. We left that area and went back to camp to see if Bill was there. Bill was not in camp. I gathered everyone and told them to look and find him and to put on their pistols. We looked for about an hour but Bill disappeared, not to be found.

I took Daz with me and went back to the place where we make the casts to see if there were any track that could be found. I happened to be a good tracker because of the Native American blood that I have in me. We did find something: there seemed to have been a scuffle off to the right of the tracks in the tree line, so something did happen. I just hoped that Bill was alright. There was nothing that could be done about Bill. The expedition must go on without Rattlesnake Bill. We were not supposed to lose any lives on this trip. We went back to camp and let everyone know about Bill. That put everyone on edge.

We started to be more aware of our surroundings, the things in and around the camp. Daz said to me that he was smelling a skunky smell and I said to him that the Bigfoot must have found our camp and to be on the alert to let the others know, too. I was very concerned about what was going to happen that night as we slept. The Bigfoot are mostly nocturnal, so that's when they come out to make an appearance. There are many stories that Bigfoot attack at night or go into camps.

During the night we heard lots of footsteps walking around the campsite. There was something else—in the woods about quarter mile away there was a bright light on the ground. We as a group went to see what it was, and we were all shocked. We saw a UFO that landed on the ground. As we got closer to it, it took off. I have read that there may be a connection with UFO's and Bigfoot, that the Bigfoots were seeded here. We don't know what happened to Bill; maybe the UFO abducted him.

The next day we started out early to look for a spot that fit our needs to set the trap, now that we knew that the Bigfoot were here. We needed a spot near a medium-sized tree, that we could pull down, that could hold the weight of a Bigfoot. It also had to be on flat ground so we could place the net on the ground with trip wires, which will spring the trap closed and lift the net holding the Bigfoot. All of this had to be done and then we would use the tranquilizer guns to knock out the animal and fly him to the waiting scientists.

Chapter 5

It was hard trying to find the correct spot for the trap. Either the ground was too steep or there wasn't the right size tree to hold the weight of Bigfoot. We didn't find a spot that day and we were not looking forward to the night when the Bigfoot are out and about. The night started out quiet. Arkansas Tom Willis started the campfire and we were all very still when Tom said to all of us, "I have the feeling that we are being watched again." Matt Smith said that he was picking up on the skunky smell, too. That's when small rocks were being thrown at us—not trying to hit us, just being thrown to make us aware of their presence. This went on for about an hour and then it stopped. It was getting late and we had a long, tough day, so we went to bed in our tents. In the middle of the night we heard footsteps in our camp. We dared not take a look to see what it was expect for Daz; he poked his head out of his tent and with his flashlight he saw eyes shining at about ten feet high, a creature with shoulders four feet wide and arms hanging to below its knees. Daz quickly turned off the light. The

Bigfoot started to make sounds and another one that was in the tree line was answering him and I think there was a third one on the other side of the camp. If they attacked it would be an ugly scene. During the night I was trying to contact the Bigfoot telepathically to let them know we didn't mean them any harm, but to no avail. I have read that they will communicate with people through their mind. I was hoping that they would read me as a good person and not do us any harm.

We didn't sleep much that night and in the morning the camp was filled with tracks and small rocks. We had better find that spot for the trap as fast as we could. We were in Bigfoot territory and they will defend it.

In the mean time we were all concerned about Bill and his whereabouts, what really happened to him, and if something else was going to happen before we could set the trap up. Also, what about the UFO that was so very close to camp the night before? Was there a connection between the UFO and the Bigfoot? Could the aliens in the UFO read our minds and our plans for the Bigfoot? All of these things were going through everyone's mind.

It was time to call in the helicopter to the area where it will be needed. I called Jimmy P to get the helicopter ready and up to the Lake. I gave Jimmy P. the coordinates of the lake where we were. We found a clearing where the copter could land and wait for the trap to close once it was set up.

It should only take a few hours for the copter to arrive. It was also time to call Dr. Rivas and his team of scientists who would do all of the work to catalog a new species of animal. I had been in contact with Dr. Rivas and his team consisted of a geneticist, microbiologist, biologist, and two scientists from the American Museum of Natural History. The helicopter would pick up the scientific team on the way up to the lake. All things were starting to fall into place. But would the Bigfoot cooperate?

Chapter 6

All things were at the ready for the action to start. The trap was set, the tranquilizer guns were at the ready, the team that I bought was ready, the bait was at a height where only the Bigfoot could grab the bait food and set off the tap—all things were a go. We set the trap for the Bigfoot to get caught and now it became a waiting game. The only problem that I could see was that the Bigfoot are nocturnal and we had to trap the Bigfoot during the day. We weren't prepared to trap him in the dark of night, so it had to be done during the day.

It was going to be a long wait.

The minutes turned to hours and hours into days. My team was getting jumpy waiting for something to happen. I didn't know what to do to get the Bigfoot to get around the trap. I must think of something since we were running out of time. The expedition was running out of time. My team was only going to be here for a few more days before they had to get back to their normal life and back to working again.

I then remembered seeing a TV show that said that the Bigfoot are attracted to women's voices because of the higher pitch. It looked like I had to call my wife, Toni, and she needed to get one of her friends to come to the lake to attract a Bigfoot.

I had to find a spot where there was reception for the cell phone.

"Hi, Toni, I need your help. I need you to come up to the lake here and you need to bring a girlfriend up with you."

Toni said, "Why?"

"'cause the Bigfoot are not going near the trap and the only thing that I can think of is getting two women to come to the lake and maybe that will draw the Bigfoot to the trap.

Toni said, "I will try to get off from work, but to ask one of my friends to drop everything and come up to the lake is an unknown."

I asked, "Can you please try? This will be our only shot to complete this expedition successfully."

"Okay, I will try to find one of my friends, but no promises. I will get back to you as soon as I know something."

"Okay, honey, and thanks." Toni called her friend Tamera and she said that she was willing to help us out. So within a few hours they were on their way to the camp.

The waiting was the most taxing thing. I was able to arrange the helicopter to pick up the girls and bring them to the trap. So by the next day, they were here at the trap and now we could put everything into action, I hoped. The biggest question was would this work?

Chapter 7

As we were waiting and the girls were talking near the trap, we started to smell a very skunky odor and we realized that the Bigfoot were around now and we all got ready to go into action. Everyone knew what his job was and how and when to go into action.

We heard branches snapping in the woods and the sound was coming closer to us. The smell was getting really strong now so we knew the Bigfoot was close.

All of a sudden the Bigfoot was running out of the woods and was going towards the girls and we thought it wanted to grab one of the girls as he ran. The Bigfoot ran right into the trap and when he did that he sprung the trap. The net went up in the air just as planed and my team went into action. The two team members shot their tranquilizer guns and both hit the marks and within a few minutes the Bigfoot was out. I radioed the helicopter. It flew in, we hooked up the net to the rope that the copter had dropped, and off the copter went to the waiting scientists, who were aware that the copter was on its way with a real live Bigfoot.

Everything worked as planned. No harm was done to the Bigfoot; he was returned to his forest and the scientific research was completed and cataloged. All was done, except we lost a man: Rattlesnake Bill was taken by the UFO. We were all saddened about his loss, but he died doing what he loved to do.

As night fell over the camp, we were reminiscing about all the things that happened to us and the fact that now the world of science was saying that the Bigfoot are real.

As time passed again we saw a bright light in the woods and we knew it was another UFO and we grabbed our things and went after it. By the time we arrived to the spot where the UFO was, it was gone. Lying on the ground was Rattlesnake Bill. He was dropped off by the UFO. We got back to camp and Bill seemed to be fine for what he went through and doesn't remember what happened when he was taken. They wiped out his memory of the ordeal, which was a good thing. The expedition was a complete success and no one lost their lives and we could all go back to what we were doing before this adventure happened.

Watch out for another thrilling adventure
in the life of Jake Hawks.

Tree Structures

Snap Offs

Milton Keynes UK
Ingram Content Group UK Ltd.
UKHW040639070923
428220UK00004B/193